1·25

Edition Eulenburg

No. 403

SCHUBERT

SYMPHONY No. 8

D. 759

Unfinished — Inachevée — Unvollendet

B minor — Si mineur — H moll

Ernst Eulenburg, Ltd.

London - Zürich - New York

8389

Edition Eulenburg

CHAMBER MUSIC

Edition Eulenburg

SYMPHONY No. 8

B minor
(Unfinished)

by

FRANZ SCHUBERT

Composition begun October 1822

Deutsch No. 759

First performed 17th December, 1865,
Gesellschaft der Musikfreunde at Vienna
under the direction of Joh. Herbeck

Edited with Foreword by
MAX HOCHKOFLER

Ernst Eulenburg, Ltd. London, W.1.
Edition Eulenburg, G,m.b.H., Zürich
Edition Eulenburg, Inc. New York

E 1961/7

Schubert: Symphony No. 8 in b minor ("Unfinished")

Schubert completed his Symphony in b minor on 30th October 1822, which is to say that on that day the first two movements were finished in their final, neat manuscript. The nine initial bars of the Scherzo were sketched in full score, and the short score (piano version) had reached the beginning of the Trio. Of the Trio itself only 16 bars were sketched in their melodic line without any harmonisation whatever. This fragment, however, is sufficient proof of Schubert's original intention to complete the work in its customary four-movement form. Why the symphony never was completed is one of the many riddles which Schubert has left for posterity with his "Unfinished". (A somewhat similar case within the wealth of Schubert's creative output might be cited: There exists a fragment of a second movement —Andante—to follow the great Quartet Movement in c minor of 1820.)

Nevertheless Schubert has created, with his b minor symphony, a masterwork which places him into the ranks of the greatest symphonic composers for all eternity. And the fate of the score of the "Unfinished" is a true parallel to the tragedy mirrored within.

Anselm Hüttenbrenner (1794-1868), born in Graz, had been Schubert's co-student with the Court Composer Antonio Salieri since 1815. A sincere and lasting friendship sprang up between these two young students, which continued even when Hüttenbrenner returned to his native Graz in 1821, where later on he became the director of the Styrian Music Association, and whereas Schubert's music was hardly ever heard in public in Vienna, it was performed with ever increasing success in Graz from 1820 onwards in the concerts of this Music Association. On 10th April 1823 the Styrian Music Association acknowledged Schubert's

Schuberts h-moll-Symphonie wurde am 30.Oktober 1822 vollendet, was soviel besagen will, dass die 2 ersten Sätze in sauberer Handschrift fertig vorlagen. Vom Scherzo waren die 9 Anfangstakte partiturmässig aufgezeichnet, während ein Klavierauszug hierzu bis zum Trio gediehen war; von diesem selbst ist nur der erste Teil in seinem melodischen Verlauf, 16 Takte umfassend, ohne jegliche Harmonisierung skizziert. Durch dieses Fragment ist jedoch Schuberts ursprüngliche Absicht hinreichend bezeugt, das Werk in herkömmlicher Weise auszubauen. Dass es nicht dazu gekommen ist, wird wohl für immer eines der vielen Rätsel bleiben, die Schubert nicht nur mit der "Unvollendeten" der Nachwelt hinterlassen hat. Um hierfür ein ähnliches Beispiel aus seinem immensen Schaffen anzuführen, sei auf den grandiosen c-moll-Quartettsatz aus dem Jahr 1820 hingewiesen, wovon ein Andante als 2. Satz ebenfalls ein Torso geblieben ist.

Trotzdem hat Schubert mit der h-moll-Symphonie ein Meisterwerk geschaffen, das seinen Namen auch auf diesem Gebiet für alle Zeiten denen der grössten Tonschöpfer zugesellt. Der inneren Tragik der "Unvollendeten" steht das äussere Geschick dieser Partitur treulich zur Seite.

Der aus Graz gebürtige Anselm Hüttenbrenner (1794-1868) war seit 1815 gleichzeitig mit Schubert Schüler des Komponisten und damaligen k.k.Hofkapellmeisters Antonio Salieri in Wien. Zwischen den beiden Scholaren entwickelte sich eine herzliche und innige Freundschaft, die auch weiterhin unvermindert fortbestand, als Hüttenbrenner anfangs 1821 in seine Vaterstadt zurückkehren musste und bald darauf die künstlerische Leitung des Steiermärkischen Musikvereins übernahm. Während in Wien Schubert in öffentlichen Konzerten kaum zu Worte kam,

musical greatness by appointing him an Honorary Member of the Association. When the Diploma reached Vienna, Schubert was on tour with the opera singer Johann Michael Vogl, that great interpreter of his songs, from which he only returned in September. On 20th September 1823 Schubert expressed his gratitude in the following letter:

"Esteemed Music Association!

My deepest gratitude for the Diploma of Honorary Membership, which you so kindly sent me and which, owing to a prolonged absence from Vienna, I only received a few days ago. May I succeed by my zeal within the art of music one day to become truly worthy of this distinction. In order to give further and musical expression to the intensity of my gratitude, I shall take the liberty of presenting your esteemed association with a score of one of my symphonies at an early date.

With greatest admiration I am the grateful servant at the disposal of a highly respected association.

Franz Schubert".

Much time passed before Schubert redeemed his promise, and it was only at the stern admonition of his father that Schubert sent the score of the b minor symphony to his old friend Anselm Hüttenbrenner through the latter's brother Joseph in autumn 1824. One would think that hereby the riddle of the dedication had found its solution —but in reality we come up against a new mystery in the history of this masterwork: For Anselm Hüttenbrenner secretly kept the score to himself and made a two-piano reduction of the work. This behaviour throws a curious light on the character of Hüttenbrenner, though latterly much has been done to find an honourable explanation. One opinion, which has been voiced amongst others, is that Schubert would hardly have chosen an incomplete work (which,

wurden seine Kompositionen in Graz seit 1820 durch diesen Verein mit steigendem Erfolg zur Aufführung gebracht. In Anerkennung der "Verdienste um die Tonkunst" ernannte der Steiermärkische Musikverein Schubert am 10.April 1823 zum auswärtigen Ehrenmitglied. Als das Diplom in Wien eintraf, war Schubert mit Hof-Opernsänger Johann Michael Vogl, dem grossartigen Interpreten seiner Lieder, auf einer ausgedehnten Konzertreise durch Oberösterreich unterwegs, von der beide erst Mitte September zurückkehrten. Schubert dankte am 20. September 1823 mit folgendem Schreiben:

"Löblicher Musikverein!

Für das mir gütigst übersandte Ehrenmitglieds-Diplom, welches ich übrigens wegen langer Abwesenheit von Wien erst vor einigen Tagen erhielt, danke ich verbindlichst. Möchte es meinem Eifer für die Tonkunst gelingen, dieser Auszeichnung einst völlig würdig zu werden. Um auch in Tönen meinen lebhaften Dank auszudrücken, werde ich mir die Freyheit nehmen, dem löblichen Verein ehestens eine meiner Symphonien in Partitur zu überreichen.

Mit ausgezeichnetster Hochachtung eines löblichen Vereines dankergebenster, bereitwilligster Diener

Franz Schubert".

Die Einlösung des Versprechens liess lange auf sich warten. Es bedurfte der eindringlichsten Mahnung seines Vaters, dass Schubert im Herbst 1824 die angekündigte Partitur—es war die h-moll-Symphonie—seinem alten Freunde Anselm Hüttenbrenner durch dessen Bruder Joseph zuschickte. Man möchte nun glauben, die Angelegenheit der Dedikation habe damit ihre endgiltige Lösung gefunden. Aber hier beginnt ein neues Mysterium in der Geschichte dieses Meisterwerks. Denn Anselm Hüttenbrenner behielt die Partitur für sich und verheimlichte den Besitz derselben, von der er auch einen

in addition, did not bear a written dedication) as a token of gratitude for the honorary membership, and that therefore Hüttenbrenner had been completely justified in regarding the score as his own, personal property. It was only in 1860 that Hüttenbrenner's brother Joseph, in a letter, drew the attention of the Viennese conductor Johann Herbeck to this treasure, and strangely enough Herbeck, though well-known as a Schubert enthusiast, allowed five years to elapse before collecting this unique work from Hüttenbrenner's library on 1st May 1865. He then gave it its first performance on 17th December 1865 in a concert of the Gesellschaft der Musikfreunde in Vienna. Since then the "Unfinished", the "finished" work of one of the greatest composers of all time, has conquered the whole world.

For the sake of completeness, the fragments of the third movement mentioned earlier on have been appended to this score.

Dr. Max Hochkofler

Salzburg, 3rd March, 1961

Klavierauszug zu 4 Händen anfertigte Dieses Gebahren wirft ein merkwürdige Zwielicht auf den Charakter Hütten brenners, zu dessen Ehrenrettung i jüngster Vergangenheit mancherlei un ternommen wurde. So konnte ma beispielsweise vernehmen, dass Schube wohl kaum ein unvollendetes Werk obendrein "ohne Widmungsvermerk" als Dank für die Ehrenmitgliedschaf ausersehen habe, und diesem Tatbestan zufolge Hüttenbrenner berechtigt ge wesen sei, die Partitur *bona fide* als sei Eigentum zu betrachten. Erst im Jahr 1860 wurde durch den Bruder Anselms Joseph Hüttenbrenner, der Wiener Hof Kapellmeister Johann Herbeck in einen Brief auf diesen "Schatz" aufmerksar gemacht; verwunderlicherweise liess sic der als Schubert-Enthusiast bekannt Hof-Kapellmeister 5 Jahre Zeit, diese einzigartige Werk am 1.Mai 1865 au Hüttenbrenners Bibliothek abzuholer das dann unter Herbecks Leitung ar 17.Dezember desselben Jahres in einer Konzert der Gesellschaft der Musik freunde in Wien die Uraufführun erlebte.

Seither hat die "Unvollendete" al vollendete Schöpfung eines der grösste Genien der Musik die ganze We erobert.

Der Vollständigkeit halber wurde der vorliegenden Partitur auch di eingangs erwähnten Fragmente des 3 Satzes angeschlossen. Salzburg, 3.Mär 1961. Dr. Max Hochkofle

"Unfinished" Symphony

I

Allegro moderato

Franz Schubert, Op. posth.
1797-1828

2 Flauti
2 Oboi
2 Clarinetti in A
2 Fagotti
2 Corni in D
2 Trombe in E
1.2. } 3 Tromboni
3.
Timpani in H-Fis
Violino I
Violino II
Viola
Violoncello
Contrabasso

N.º 403   E.E. 3603   Ernst Eulenburg Ltd.,
London · Zurich

8

E.E. 3603

E.E. 3603

E.E. 3603

300

II

Andante con moto

E. E. 3603

48

60

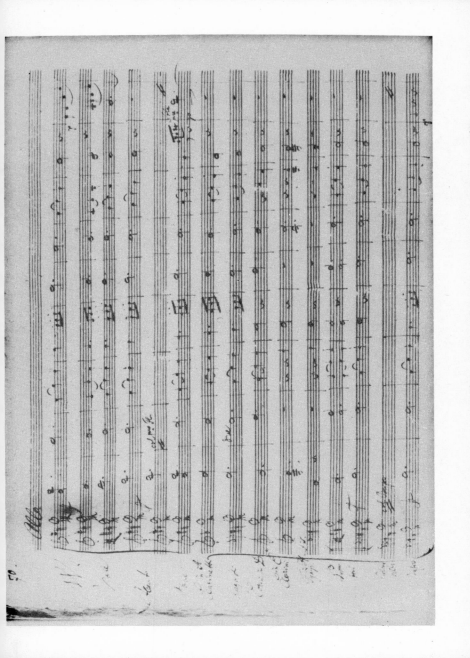

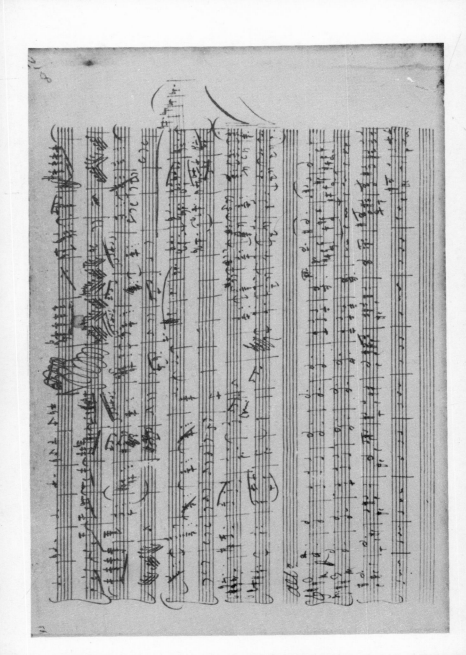

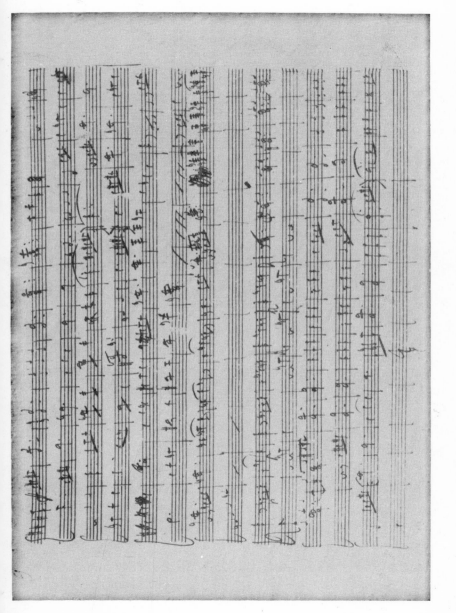

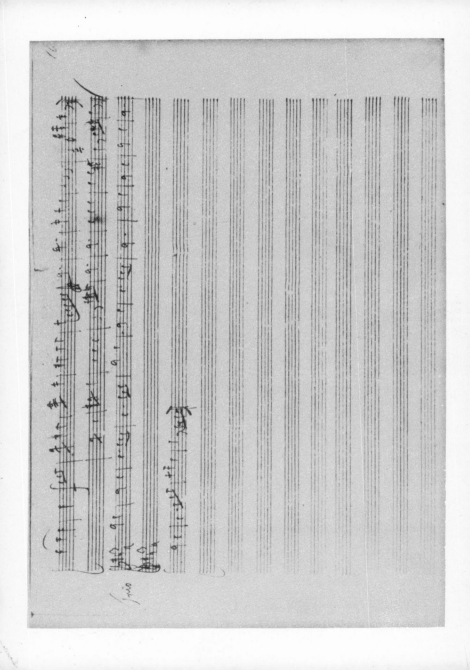

CHAMBER MUSIC—contd.

No.

281. **Bach,** Brandenburg, Concerto No.4, G
282. **Bach,** Brandenburg, Concerto No.5, D
284. **Smetana,** Quartet, D m
285. **H. Wolf,** Quartet, D m
286. **H. Wolf,** Ital. Serenade f. Quartet, G..
287. **Reger,** Flute-Trio, (Serenade) op. 77a, D
288. **Reger,** String-Trio, op. 77b, A m....
292. **Strauss,** Piano-Quartet, op. 13, C m..
293. **Reger,** Quartet, op. 109, E♭
294. **Sibelius,** Quartet, op. 56, D m (Voces Intimae)
295. **Reger,** Piano-Quartet, op. 113, D m..
296. **Reger,** Sextet, op. 118, F
297. **Beethoven,** Quartet, F. after Son. op 14, 1
298. **Dvořák,** Quartet, op. 34, D m
299. **Dvořák,** Quartet, op. 51, E♭
300. **Dvořák,** Quartet, op. 61, C
301. **Dvořák,** Quartet, op. 80, E
302. **Dvořák,** Quartet, op. 96, F
303. **Dvořák,** Quartet, op. 105, A♭
304. **Dvořák,** Quartet, op. 106, G
305. **Dvořák,** Piano-Quintet, op. 81, A
306. **Dvořák,** String-Quintet, op. 97, Es
308. **Mozart,** Serenade f. 8 Wind, E♭ [375].
309. **Mozart,** Serenade f. 8 Wind, C m [388]
310. **Bruckner,** Quintet, F
312. **Reger,** Flute-Trio, (Seren.) op. 141a, G
313. **Reger,** String-Trio, op. 141b, D m....
314. **Reger,** Quartet, op. 121, F♯ m
317. **Grieg,** Quartet, F (unfinished)
318. **Schönberg,** Sextet (Verkl.Nacht) op. 4
319. **Reger,** Quartet, op. 74, D m
322. **Reger,** Clarinet-Quintet, op. 146, A...
323. **Franck,** Quartet, D
324. **Pfitzner,** Piano-Quintet, op. 23, C....
329. **Franck,** Piano-Quintet, F m
330. **Dvořák,** Piano-Quartet, op. 87, E♭ ...

No.

331. **Dvořák,** Piano-Trio, op. 65, F m
332. **Dvořák,** Piano-Trio, op. 90, E m (Dumky)
333. **Reger,** Piano-Quartet, op. 133, A m.
334. **Schönberg,** Quartet, op. 7, D m
335. **Smetana,** Piano-Trio, op. 15, G m...
336. **Reger,** Piano-Quintet, op. posth., C m
337. **Dvořák,** Sextet, op. 48, A
338. **Dvořák,** Quintet, op. 77, G
339. **Dohnányi,** Quartet, op. 15, D♭
340. **Reger,** Piano-Quintet, op. 64, C m
341. **Saint-Saëns,** Piano-Trio, op. 18, F..
342. **Saint-Saëns,** Piano-Quint., op. 14, A m
343. **Dohnányi,** Piano-Quintet, op. 26, E♭ m
347. **Mozart,** Horn Quintet, E♭ [407]
348. **Corelli,** Christmas Conc.
349. **Mozart,** Divertimento No. 11, D [251
351. **Mozart,** Divertimento No. 13, F [253
352. **Mozart,** Divertimento No. 14, B♭ [270
353. **Schubert,** Quartet, op. posth., D
354. **Schubert,** Quartet movement, op. posth., C m
355. **Haydn,** Quartet, op. 77, 2, F
356. **Haydn,** Quartet, op. 103, B♭
357. **Corelli,** Concerto grosso No. 1, D
358. **Corelli,** Concerto grosso No. 3, C m
359. **Corelli,** Concerto grosso No. 9, F
360. **Franck,** Piano-Trio, op. 1, 1, F♯m
361. **Geminiani,** Concerto grosso No. 1, D
362. **Geminiani,** Concerto grosso No. 2, G m
363. **Geminiani,** Concerto grosso No. 3, E m
364. **Geminiani,** Concerto grosso No. 4, D m
365. **Geminiani,** Concerto grosso No. 5, B♭
366. **Geminiani,** Concerto grosso No. 6, E m
367. **Malipiero,** Quartet (Cantàri alla Madrigalesca)
368. **Zilcher,** Suite f. Quartet

OPERAS

901. **Wagner,** Rienzi
902. **Wagner,** Flying Dutchman
903a. **Wagner,** Tannhäuser
903b. **Wagner,** Variants of Paris Arrgmt.
904. **Wagner,** Lohengrin
905. **Wagner,** Tristan und Isolde
906. **Wagner,** Mastersingers of Nuremberg
907. **Wagner,** Rhinegold
908. **Wagner,** The Valkyrie
909. **Wagner,** Siegfried

910. **Wagner,** Twilight of the Gods
911. **Wagner,** Parsifal
912. **Mozart,** Magic Flute
913. **Humperdinck,** Hänsel und Gretel
914. **Beethoven,** Fidelio
915. **Weber,** Der Freischütz
916. **Mozart,** Nozze di Figaro
917. **Gluck,** Iphigenie en Tauride
918. **Mozart,** Don Giovanni

CHORAL WORKS

951. **Beethoven,** Missa solemnis
953. **Bach,** St. Matthew Passion
954. **Mozart,** Requiem
955. **Haydn,** The Creation
956. **Händel,** The Messiah
959. **Bach,** High Mass, B m
960. **Bruckner,** Te Deum
961. **Bruckner,** Great Mass, F m
962. **Bach,** Christmas Orat.
963. **Palestrina,** Missa Papae Marcelli
964. **Bach,** Magnificat
965. **Bach,** St. John, Passion
966. **Palestrina,** Stabat Mater

968. **Reger,** Der 100. Psalm
969. **Brahms,** Requiem
970. **Schubert,** Mass No. 6, E♭
972. **Bruckner,** The 150th Psalm
973. **Pergolesi,** Stabat Mater
974. **Schubert,** Mass No. 5, A♭
975. **Verdi,** Requiem
976. **Schütz,** St. Matthew, Passion
977. **Schütz,** Seven Words of Christ
978. **Schütz,** St. Luke, Passion
979. **Schütz,** St, John, Passion
980. **Schütz,** Resurrection History
981. **Schütz,** Christmas History